ISBN 0-914850-10-5
MO582

I am a Promise

Illustrated by Aletha Jones

by
Bill & Gloria Gaither

impact
books

I am a promise,
I am a possibility,

I am a prom-ise,— I am a pos-si-bil-i-ty,

I am a promise with a capital "P";

I am a prom-ise__ with a cap-i-tal "P";__

I can be anything—
anything God wants me to be.

You are a promise,

You are a prom-ise,   You are a pos-si-bil-i-ty;___

You are a possibility;

You are a promise with a capital "P",

You are a great big bundle of potentiality.

You are a great big bun-dle of po-ten-ti-al-i-ty.____

9

And if you lis‑ten   you'll hear God's voice,—

**And if you listen
you'll hear God's voice,**

And if you're tryin'
He'll help you make the right choices;

and if you're try-in' He'll help you make the right choic - es;

You're a promise to be anything
He wants you to be.

12   You're a prom-ise to be____ an-y-thing He wants you to be.____

You can go an-y-where_ that He wants you to go,—

You can go anywhere that He wants you to go,

You can be anything that He wants you to be,

You can be an-y-thing___ that He wants you to be,___

You can climb the high mountain,

You can cross the wide sea,

You can climb the high moun - tain, You can cross the wide sea,

You're a great big promise, you see!

You're a great big prom-ise, you see!

**I am a promise,
I am a possibility;**

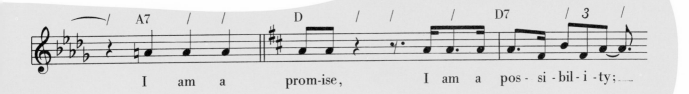

I am a prom-ise, I am a pos - si - bil - i -ty;

I am a prom-ise with a cap - i - tal "P",

I am a great big bun -dle of po -ten - ti - al - i - ty.

20

I am a promise with a capital "P",
I am a great big bundle of potentiality.

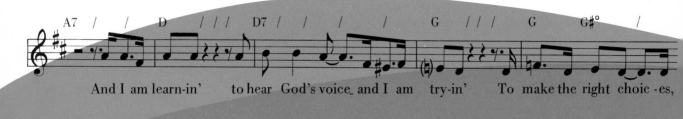

And I am learn-in' to hear God's voice and I am try-in' To make the right choic-es,

And I am learnin' to hear God's voice

**And I am tryin'
to make the right choices,**

I'm a prom-ise to be, ___ an-y-thing God wants me to be. ___

I'm a promise to be,
anything God wants me to be.

So keep on list'nin' to hear God's voice

So keep on list'-nin' to hear God's voice and keep on try-in', He'll help you make the right choic-es,

And keep on tryin', He'll help you make the right choices,

You're a promise to be, anything He wants,

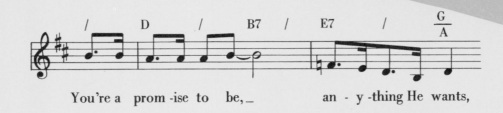

You're a prom-ise to be,— an-y-thing He wants,

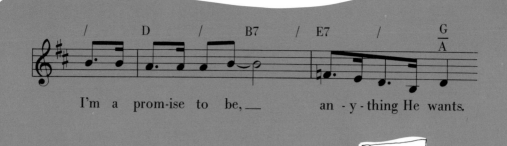

I'm a promise to be,
anything He wants.

You're a promise to be anything;

You're a   prom - ise to   be___   an-y -thing;_

Anything!
He wants you to be.

Spoken An-y-thing!   He wants you to   be. _____